PRINTED TEST BANK

DAVID HARRIS
Trident Technical College

INTRODUCTION TO TECHNICAL MATHEMATICS

FIFTH EDITION

Allyn J. Washington
Dutchess Community College

Mario F. Triola
Dutchess Community College

Ellena E. Reda
Dutchess Community College

PEARSON
Addison
Wesley

Boston   San Francisco   New York
London   Toronto   Sydney   Tokyo   Singapore   Madrid
Mexico City   Munich   Paris   Cape Town   Hong Kong   Montreal

Reproduced by Pearson Addison-Wesley from electronic files supplied by the author.

Copyright © 2008 Pearson Education, Inc.
Publishing as Pearson Addison-Wesley, 75 Arlington Street, Boston, MA 02116.

ISBN-13: 978-0-321-45066-1
ISBN-10: 0-321-45066-3

1 2 3 4 5 6 OPM 10 09 08 07

PEARSON

Addison
Wesley

Table of Contents

Chapter 1 Signed Numbers   1

Chapter 2 Units of Measurement and Significant Digits   5

Chapter 3 Introduction to Algebra   9

Chapter 4 Equations and Inequalities   13

Chapter 5 Graphs   17

Chapter 6 Geometry   23

Chapter 7 Simultaneous Equations   29

Chapter 8 Factoring   33

Chapter 9 Rational Expressions   37

Chapter 10 Radical Expressions   41

Chapter 11 Quadratic Equations   45

Chapter 12 Exponential and Logarithmic Expressions   49

Chapter 13 Right Angle Trigonometry   53

Chapter 14 Oblique Triangles and Vectors   57

Chapter 15 Graphs of Trigonometric Functions   61

Chapter 16 Complex Numbers   64

Chapter 17 Data Analysis   69

Answers to Printed Test Bank   73

CHAPTER 1 **FORM A**	TECHNICAL MATH
NAME:_____	SECTION:_____

Perform the indicated operation

1. $(-4)+12$

1._____

2. $-3-3+7$

2._____

3. $5^2-3(13-7)$

3._____

4. $8-3(6+(-2))$

4._____

5. $\dfrac{4(-2)(3)}{(2)(-1)}$

5._____

6. -4^2+16

6._____

7. $\left(\dfrac{3}{4}\right)^2$

7._____

8. $-\left(-\dfrac{2}{5}\right)^2$

8._____

9. $\left|2(4-2)^2-10\right|$

9._____

10. $\dfrac{3.25^2+\sqrt{12}}{2(3.1)^2}$ Round to the nearest thousandth .

10._____

11. $\sqrt{2.25+4.1^2}$ Round to the nearest hundredth.

11._____

12. Express 17,400,000,000 using scientific notation.

12._____

13. Express 0.00000043 using scientific notation.

13._____

14. Express 2.17×10^7 as an ordinary number.   14. _____

15. Add: $(7.34 \times 10^5) + (2.2 \times 10^4)$ 15. _____

16. Subtract: (5.67×10^{-4}) from (9.9×10^{-3}) 16. _____

17. Multiply: $(3.6 \times 10^5)(2.4 \times 10^3)$ 17. _____

18. Divide: $\dfrac{(1.2 \times 10^{-4})}{(4.8 \times 10^2)}$ 18. _____

19. On a recent math test a student missed 4 True/False questions worth 2 points a piece and 3 word problems worth 2.5 points each. If the total number of points possible was 100, what was the student's score?

19._____

20. An engineer needs to find the time it will take for his new computer to do 50 billion calculations. If it takes his new computer 2.6×10^{-13} seconds to do one calculation, how long will it take to do the 50 billion calculations? Leave your answer in scientific notation.

20._____

CHAPTER 1 **FORM B**   TECHNICAL MATH

NAME:_____   SECTION:_____

Perform the indicated operation

1. $(-5)+11$ 1._____

2. $-4-4+9$ 2._____

3. $4^2-3(13-10)$ 3._____

4. $7-3(5+(-3))$ 4._____

5. $\dfrac{5(-2)(3)}{(3)(-1)}$ 5._____

6. -5^2+25 6._____

7. $\left(\dfrac{2}{5}\right)^2$ 7._____

8. $-\left(-\dfrac{3}{4}\right)^2$ 8._____

9. $\left|3(4-6)^2-10\right|$ 9._____

10. $\dfrac{2.75^2+\sqrt{20}}{3(2.1)^2}$ Round to the nearest thousandth .   10._____

11. $\sqrt{3.5+4.3^2}$ Round to the nearest hundredth.   11._____

12. Express 14,700,000,000 using scientific notation.   12._____

13. Express 0.0000034 using scientific notation.   13._____

14. Express 7.12×10^5 as an ordinary number.   14. _____

15. Add: $(3.74 \times 10^5) + (3.2 \times 10^4)$ 15. _____

16. Subtract: (6.57×10^{-4}) from (9.9×10^{-3}) 16. _____

17. Multiply: $(4.3 \times 10^5)(5.2 \times 10^3)$ 17. _____

18. Divide: $\dfrac{(1.2 \times 10^{-5})}{(4.8 \times 10^{-2})}$ 18. _____

19. On a recent math test a student missed 5 True/False questions worth 3 points a piece and 2 word problems worth 3.5 points each. If the total number of points possible was 100, what was the student's score?

19._____

20. An engineer needs to find the time it will take for his new computer to do 75 billion calculations. If it takes his new computer 2.7×10^{-13} seconds to do one calculation, how long will it take to do the 75 billion calculations? Leave your answer in scientific notation.

20._____

CHAPTER 2 FORM A   TECHNICAL MATH

NAME:_____   SECTION:_____

1. Determine the number of significant digits
    in the number 2.403.   1._____

2. Determine the number of significant digits in the
    number 0.000034   2._____

3. Round to two significant digits: 75.87
                                                     3._____

4. Round to 3 significant digits   0.24034
                                                     4._____

5. What unit is being expressed by the abbreviation μL.
                                                     5._____

6. What is the abbreviation for the unit mV
                                                     6._____

7. Convert 6in to cm.
                                                     7._____

8. Reduce $36in^2$ to ft^2.
                                                     8._____

9. Convert 33 km/hr to miles/hr.

9._____

10. Reduce 12 feet per second to miles per hour.

10._____

11. Which number is more precise: 2.46 or 13.8.

11._____

12. Which number is more accurate: 2115 or 7.35.

12._____

13.Give the meaning of the metric unit kilogram.

13._____

14. The super skyscraper Taipei 101 currently holds the record for tallest building. It's height is listed as 449 meters. Convert this to feet.

14._____

15. In electronics the unit of watts is found by multiplying the current, in amperes, by the voltage, in volts. Find the power of a circuit with a current of 0.00125 amperes and a voltage of 1.438 volts. Round to the proper degree of accuracy.

15._____

CHAPTER 2 FORM B

CHAPTER 2 FORM B   TECHNICAL MATH

NAME:_____   SECTION:_____

1. Determine the number of significant digits in the
   number 12.002   1._____

2. Determine the number of significant digits in the
   number 0.00017   2._____

3. Round to two significant digits: 1.52
                                                   3._____

4. Round to 3 significant digits   10.903
                                                   4._____

5. What unit is being expressed by the
   abbreviation $M\Omega$.   5._____

6. What is the abbreviation for the unit millivolts.
                                                   6._____

7. Convert 12.32 in to cm.
                                                   7._____

8. Reduce 72 in^2 to ft^2 .
                                                   8._____

9. Convert 33 kilometers per hour to miles per hour.
                                                   9._____

10. Reduce 18 feet per second to miles per hour.

10._____

11. Which number is more precise: 6.42 or 81.3

11._____

12. Which number is more accurate: 2007 or 7.12.

12._____

13. Give the meaning of the metric unit milliliter.

13._____

14. The super skyscraper Taipei 101 currently holds the record for tallest building. It's height is listed as 509 meters (from ground to top of the tower). Convert this to feet.

14._____

15. In electronics the unit of watts is found by multiplying the current, in amperes, by the voltage, in volts. Find the power of a circuit with a current of 0.00125 amperes and a voltage of 2.876 volts. Round to the proper degree of accuracy.

15._____

CHAPTER 3 FORM A   TECHNICAL MATH

NAME:_____   SECTION:_____

1. Identify the coefficient of the fourth term for the expression
$$2ab^2 - 4ab + a^3b^2 - 7a$$ 1._____

2. Identify the like terms in the expression:
$$16t^2u + 4tu^2 + 6tu - 3t^2u$$ 2._____

3. Simplify $15x^2 + 4x^2$ 3._____

4. Simplify $3xyz + 4xyz - 10xyz$ 4._____

5. Simplify $(2ab)^4 - (3a^2b^2)^2$ 5._____

6. Simplify $2(t^2 + 4t^3) - 3t^3 + 6t$ 6._____

7. Simplify $\left(3xy^2\right)\left(-2xy\right)$ 7._____

8. Simplify $(y+3)(2y-3)$ 8._____

9. Simplify $(2x)(x+4)(x-3)$ 9._____

10. Simplify $(r+5)(r-5)$ 10._____

11. Simplify $\dfrac{-16a^3b^2}{4ab^3}$ 11._____

12. Simplify $\dfrac{4a^2-6ab-9b^2}{12ab}$ 12._____

13. Simplify $\dfrac{2y^2-10y-28}{2y+4}$ 13._____

14. A certain resistor has a resistance of $r=(2r-3)(r+2)+(3r+1)(r-3)$. Simplify the right hand side of this equation.

14._____

15. The inside area of a square garden has an area of $(x+4)^2-x^2$ where x represents the length of the side of the outside of the garden. Simplify this expression.

15._____

1. Identify the coefficient of the third term for the expression
$$11xy^2 + xy - 10x^3y^2 - 17x$$ 1._____

2. Identify the like terms in the expression:
$$14w^2v - wv^2 + 3wv + 5w^2v$$ 2._____

3. Simplify $21y^2 - 3y^2$ 3._____

4. Simplify $2abc + 9abc - 15abc$ 4._____

5. Simplify $(3xy)^4 - (2x^2y^2)^2$ 5._____

6. Simplify $3(k^3 - 5k^4) + 5k^3 + 6k$ 6._____

7. Simplify $(5xy^2)(-7xy)$ 7._____

8. Simplify $(x+4)(3x-5)$ 8._____

9. Simplify $(2a)(a-2)(a+4)$ 9._____

10. Simplify $(h+4)(h-4)$ 10._____

11. Simplify $\dfrac{-36x^4y^5}{6x^2y^7}$ 11._____

12. Simplify $\dfrac{-8a^3b-12a^2b^2+20ab^4}{4ab}$ 12._____

13. Simplify $\dfrac{2a^2-10a+12}{2a-4}$ 13._____

14. A certain resistor has a resistance of $r=(r-3)(3r+2)+(5r+1)(2r-5)$. Simplify the right hand side of this equation.

                                                    14._____

15. The inside area of a square garden has an area of $(y+5)^2-y^2$ where y represents the length of the side of the outside of the garden. Simplify this expression.

                                                    15._____

CHAPTER 4 FORM A   TECHNICAL MATH

NAME:_____   SECTION:_____

Solve the given equation.

1. $3t + 20 = 5 - 2t$ 1._____

2. $\dfrac{7w - 28}{4} = -21$ 2._____

3. $2 + 3(x - 5) = 4(x - 1)$ 3._____

4. $3.1(x - 2) = 1.3x + 2.8$ 4._____

Solve the formula for the indicated letter.

5. $I = \mathrm{Pr}t;$ for t 5._____

6. $A = P + \mathrm{Pr};$ for r   6._____

7. $K = \frac{1}{2}h(a + b);$ for h 7._____

8. $F = f(1 - M);$ for M 8._____

Solve the inequalities

9. $2k - 3 \le 5$ 9._____

10. $3(y - 8) > 5y + 6$ 10._____

11. $8(5 - m) \ge 10(8 - m)$ 11._____

Find the ratio.

12.   17w to 2 w   12. _____

13.   144 in. to 3 ft.   13. _____

Solve the proportion.

14. $\dfrac{2}{3} = \dfrac{x}{180}$ 14. _____

15. $\dfrac{y+3}{12} = \dfrac{7}{6}$ 15. _____

16. $\dfrac{3}{12} = \dfrac{-1.4}{k}$ 16. _____

Solve the Problems.

17. If 7 tickets to a concert cost $92.75, how much
    are 13 tickets?

                                                                     17. _____

18.   Three hard drives have a storage capacity of 1100 gigabytes. The largest hard drive
stores twice as much as the smallest and the other stores 100 gigabytes more than the
smallest. What are the storage capacities of the largest hard drive?

                                                                     18. _____

19. A computer technician travels 210 on a service call. He averaged 40 miles per hour for
part of the trip and averaged 50 mph for the rest of the trip. If the total trip took five hours
how long did he travel at a rate of 50 miles per hour?

                                                                     19. _____

20. A company invests equal amounts of money into two investments. One pays 7% and the
other pays 8%. After one year the interest earned on the two investments is $3600. How
much was invested in each?

                                                                     20. _____

CHAPTER 4 FORM B	TECHNICAL MATH
NAME:_____	SECTION:_____

Solve the given equation.

1. $7t + 25 = 5 - 3t$

1._____

2. $\dfrac{3w - 28}{4} = -17$

2._____

3. $3 + 5(x - 5) = 4(x - 5)$

3._____

4. $3.1(x - 2) = 1.3x + 2.8$

4._____

Solve the formula for the indicated letter.

5. $I = \Pr t$; for r

5._____

6. $J = AC - 3$; for A

6._____

7. $K = \frac{1}{5}k(x + y)$; for k

7._____

8. $S = n(2 + L)$; for L

8._____

Solve the inequalities

9. $3k - 9 \le 6$

9._____

10. $5(y - 8) > 7y + 6$

10._____

11. $4(5 - n) \ge 5(8 - n)$

11._____

Find the ratio.

12.   15 mg to 4 mg   12. _____

13.   72 in. to 4 ft.   13. _____

Solve the proportion.

14. $\dfrac{3}{5} = \dfrac{x}{140}$ 14. _____

15. $\dfrac{2y+6}{24} = \dfrac{7}{6}$ 15. _____

16. $\dfrac{2}{4} = \dfrac{-2.8}{k}$ 16. _____

Solve the Problems.

17. If 6 tickets to a concert cost $70.50, how much
     are 15 tickets?

                                                                  17. _____

18.   Three hard drives have a storage capacity of 1300 gigabytes. The largest hard drive
stores twice as much as the smallest and the other stores 100 gigabytes more than the
smallest. What are the storage capacities of the largest hard drive?

                                                                  18. _____

19. A computer technician travels 220 on a service call. He averaged 40 miles per hour for
part of the trip and averaged 50 mph for the rest of the trip. If the total trip took five hours
how long did he travel at a rate of 50 miles per hour?

                                                                  19. _____

20. A company invests equal amounts of money into two investments. One pays 9% and the
other pays 6%. After one year the interest earned on the two investments is $1650. How
much was invested in each?   20. _____

CHAPTER 5 FORM A   TECHNICAL MATH

NAME:_____   SECTION:_____

1. Find $f(3)$ for the function $f(x) = -x^2 - 9$.   1._____

2. Find $f(17)$ for the function $f(x) = 4 + 2\sqrt{x-1}$.   2._____

3. What is the domain of the function $f(x) = \sqrt{x-4}$ 3._____

4. What is the domain of the function $s(t) = \dfrac{3t}{t+2}$ 4._____

Use the following figure to answer questions 5-8.

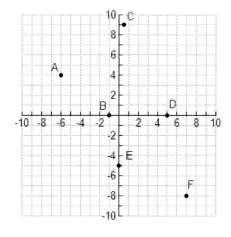

5. In which quadrant does point A lie?   5._____

6. What are the coordinates of point B?   6._____

7. Which point is a y-intercept?   7._____

8. What are the coordinates of point F?   8._____

9. Graph the function $f(x) = -\dfrac{1}{2}x - 3$.

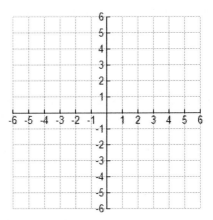

10. Graph the function $f(x) = x^2 + 2x + 1$

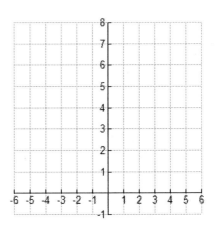

11. Find the slope of the line passing through the
     points (-2, 5) and (8, 13).   11._____

12. Calculate the x-intercept for the equation $3x + 2y = 10$

                                                    12._____

13. Calculate the y-intercept for the equation $3x + 2y = 10$

                                                    13._____

14. The height (in feet) of an object dropped off of a bridge can be modeled by the equation
$s(t) = -16t^2 + 144$. How long will it be before the object hits the water below the bridge?

14._____

15. The following graph represents the number of units a company produces and their
resulting profit. How much profit will the company make if they produce 300 units?

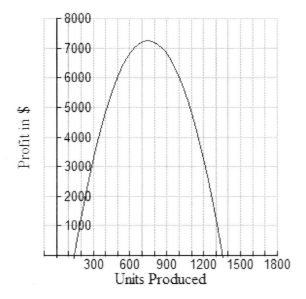

15._____

CHAPTER 5 FORM B   TECHNICAL MATH

NAME:_____   SECTION:_____

1. Find $f(4)$ for the function $f(x) = -x^2 - 16$.   1._____

2. Find $f(8)$ for the function $f(x) = 2 + 3\sqrt{x+1}$.   2._____

3. What is the domain of the function $f(x) = \sqrt{x+3}$ 3._____

4. What is the domain of the function $s(t) = \dfrac{3t}{t-3}$ 4._____

Use the following figure to answer questions 5-8.

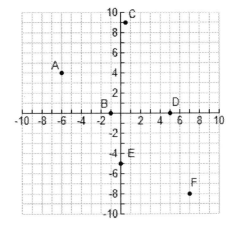

5. In which quadrant does point C lie?   5._____

6. What are the coordinates of point D?   6._____

7. Which point is an y-intercept?   7._____

8. What are the coordinates of point F?   8._____

9. Graph the function $f(x) = \dfrac{1}{3}x + 2$.

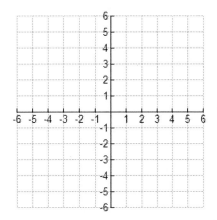

10. Graph the function $f(x) = x^2 - 4x + 4$

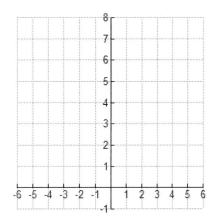

11. Find the slope of the line passing through the points (-3, 5) and (7, 13).

11._____

12. Calculate the x-intercept for the equation $4x + 3y = 8$

12._____

13. Calculate the y-intercept for the equation $4x + 3y = 8$

13._____

14. The height (in feet) of an object dropped off of a bridge can be modeled by the equation $s(t) = -36t^2 + 144$. How long will it be before the object hits the water below the bridge?

14._____

15. The following graph represents the number of units a company produces and their resulting profit. How much profit will the company make if they produce 1000 units?

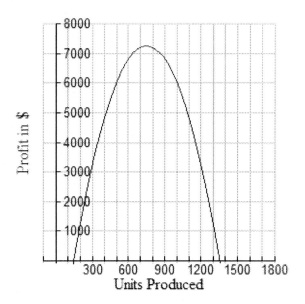

15._____

CHAPTER 6 FORM A	TECHNICAL MATH
NAME:_____	SECTION:_____

1. Convert 47°48' to decimal degrees

1._____

2. Convert 137.44° to . degrees and minutes

2._____

3. Find the perimeter of the figure below

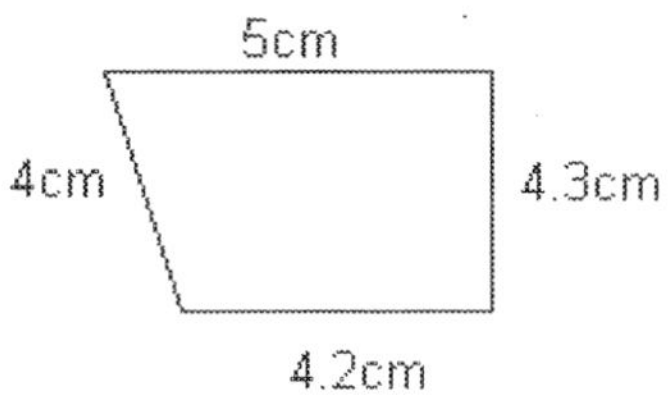

3._____

4. Find the perimeter of the figure below:

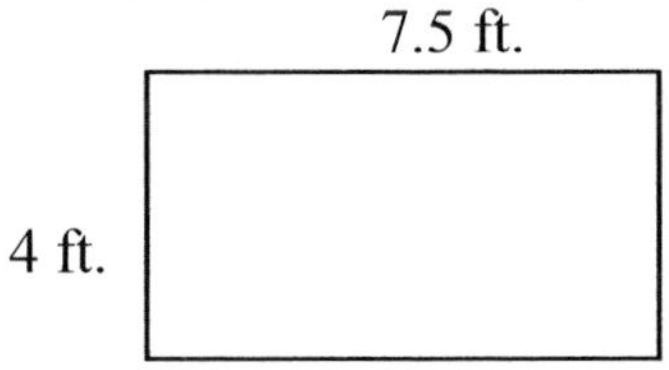

4._____

5. Find the circumference of the figure below

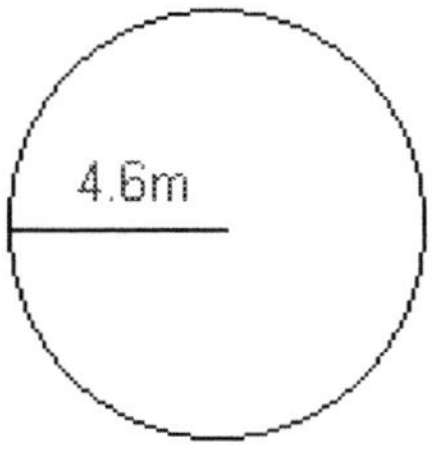

5._____

6. Find the area of the figure below.

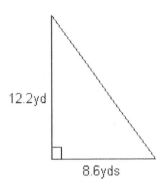

12.2yd

8.6yds

6._____

7. Find the area of the figure below.

12.3m

2.1m

7._____

8. Find the area of the figure below.

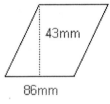

43mm

86mm

8._____

9. Find the volume of sphere with radius 12.3in.

9._____

10. Find the volume of rectangular solid measuring
     12.5cm x 13.24 cm x 2.125 cm.

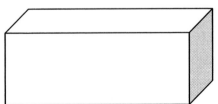

10._____

11. Find the volume of a cube with an edge of 12.43 yds.

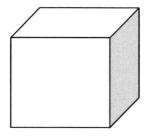

11._____

12   The owner of an older house wants to put new tile in the kitchen. At a local hardware store the tile the owner wants to put down is on sale for $2.50 per square foot. If the owners kitchen is in the shape of the figure below, how much will it cost to tile the floor?

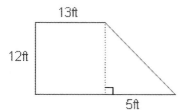

12._____

CHAPTER 6 FORM B	TECHNICAL MATH
NAME:_____	SECTION:_____

1. Convert 36°6' to decimal degrees   1._____

2. Convert 41.36° to . degrees and minutes   2._____

3. Find the perimeter of the figure below

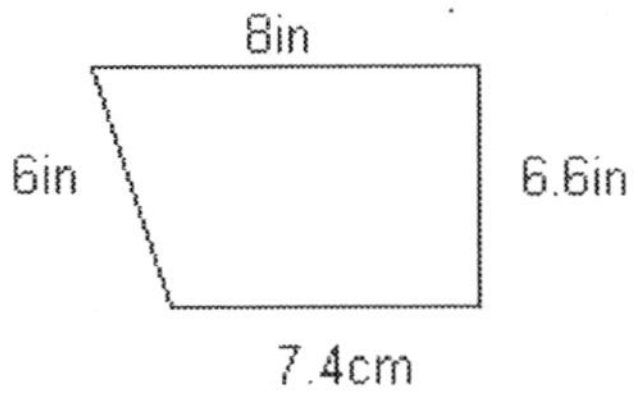

8in

6in   6.6in

7.4cm   3._____

4. Find the perimeter of the figure below:

8 ft.

3.5 ft.

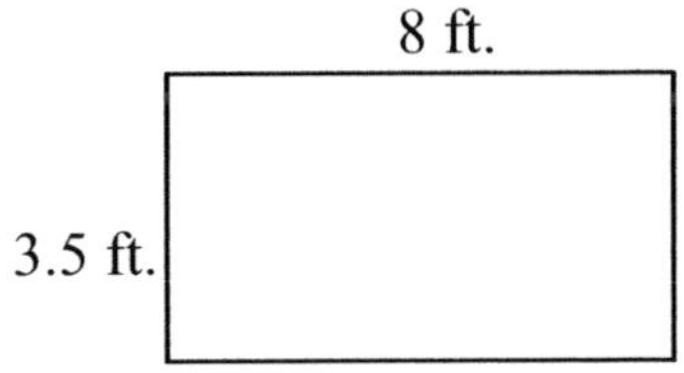

4._____

5. Find the circumference of the figure below

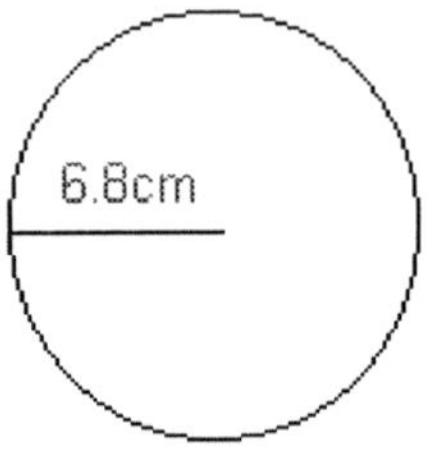

6.8cm

5._____

6. Find the area of the figure below.

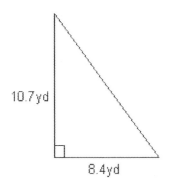

6._____

7. Find the area of the figure below.   7._____

8. Find the area of the figure below.   8._____

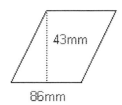

9. Find the volume of sphere with radius 10.35in.   9._____

10. Find the volume of rectangular solid measuring
    11.5cm x 13.42 cm x 3.125 cm.

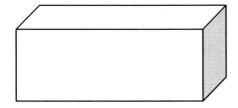

10._____

11. Find the volume of a cube with an edge of 9.57 m

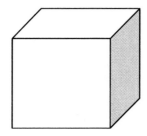

11._____

12   The owner of an older house wants to put new tile in the kitchen. At a local hardware store the tile the owner wants to put down is on sale for $3.50 per square foot. If the owners kitchen is in the shape of the figure below, how much will it cost to tile the floor?

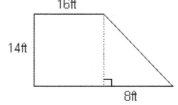

12._____

1. Graph the system of equations: $\begin{cases} x + 4y = 4 \\ 2x + 2y = 6 \end{cases}$

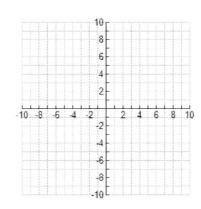

2. Solve using substitution: $\begin{cases} 2k + 3j = 10 \\ k + j = 3 \end{cases}$ 2._____

3. Solve using substitution: $\begin{cases} 2w - v = -1 \\ 2w + v = 9 \end{cases}$ 3._____

4. Solve using substitution: $\begin{cases} x - 6y = 5 \\ x - 6y = 7 \end{cases}$ 4._____

5. Solve using addition/subtraction: $\begin{cases} x - 2y = 4 \\ 2x + y = 7 \end{cases}$ 5._____

6. Solve using addition/subtraction: $\begin{cases} 2a + 3b = 6 \\ 2a - 2b = 8 \end{cases}$ 6._____

7. Solve using addition/subtraction $\begin{cases} \dfrac{1}{2}x + \dfrac{1}{3}y = 1 \\ 3x + 2y = 6 \end{cases}$ 7._____

8. Evaluate the determinant: $\begin{vmatrix} 7 & 5 \\ 2 & 2 \end{vmatrix}$

8. _____

9. Evaluate the determinant: $\begin{vmatrix} -\dfrac{1}{2} & -7 \\ \dfrac{3}{2} & 5 \end{vmatrix}$

9. _____

10. Solve using determinants $\begin{cases} a+b=-1 \\ 2a-y=4 \end{cases}$

10. _____

11. A certain type of battery cost $1.50, and another battery cost $4.00. A recent shipment contained 2200 batteries, and the bill totaled $5050. How many of the more expensive batteries were in the shipment?

11._____

12. A total of $24,000 is invested in two funds paying 9% and 11% interest. If, at year's end the interest is $1,180, how much of the $24,000 is invested at 9%?

12._____

CHAPTER 7 FORM B   TECHNICAL MATH

NAME:_____   SECTION:_____

1. Graph the system of equations: $\begin{cases} 2x+8y=8 \\ 2x+2y=6 \end{cases}$

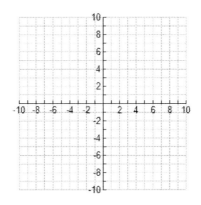

2. Solve using substitution: $\begin{cases} 2k+3j=10 \\ 2k+2j=6 \end{cases}$ 2._____

3. Solve using substitution: $\begin{cases} 2a+b=9 \\ 4a-2b=-2 \end{cases}$ 3._____

4. Solve using substitution: $\begin{cases} 5x-2y=5 \\ 5x-2y=7 \end{cases}$ 4._____

5. Solve using addition/subtraction: $\begin{cases} 2x+y=7 \\ 2x-4y=8 \end{cases}$ 5._____

6. Solve using addition/subtraction: $\begin{cases} 2a+3b=6 \\ a-b=4 \end{cases}$ 6._____

7. Solve using addition/subtraction $\begin{cases} 5x+3y=15 \\ \dfrac{1}{3}x+\dfrac{1}{5}=1 \end{cases}$ 7._____

8. Evaluate the determinant: $\begin{vmatrix} 3 & 3 \\ 5 & 7 \end{vmatrix}$ 8. _____

9. Evaluate the determinant: $\begin{vmatrix} -\dfrac{1}{3} & -4 \\ \dfrac{2}{3} & 2 \end{vmatrix}$ 9. _____

10. Solve using determinants $\begin{cases} a+b=-1 \\ 2a-y=4 \end{cases}$ 10. _____

11. A certain type of battery cost $1.50, and another battery cost $4.00. A recent shipment contained 2200 batteries, and the bill totaled $5050. How many of the cheaper batteries were in the shipment?

11. _____

12. A total of $24,000 is invested in two funds paying 9% and 11% interest. If, at year's end the interest is $1,180, how much of the $24,000 is invested at 11%?

12. _____

CHAPTER 8 FORM A

NAME:_____

TECHNICAL MATH

SECTION:_____

1. Factor: $17x^5 + 34xy^2 + 51y$ 1._____

2. Factor: $4y^2 - 8y - 2xy$ 2._____

3. Factor: $2ax + 2bx - 3a - 3b$ 3._____

4. Factor: $a^2b + a^2 - ab - a$ 4._____

5. Factor: $b^2 + 6b - 7$ 5._____

6. Factor: $x^2 - x - 12$ 6._____

7. Factor: $3y^2 - 21y + 18$ 7._____

8. Factor: $4z^2 + 13z + 3$ 8._____

9. Factor: $6k^2 + 7k + 2$ 9._____

10. Factor: $16a^3 + 40a^2 + 25a$ 10._____

11. Factor: $2a^2 - 8b^2$ 11._____

12. Factor: $m^5 - 9m$ 12._____

13. Factor: $c^3 - 27$ 13._____

14. Factor: $2y^4 + 128y$ 14._____

15. The height of a box with surface area of 108 square inches can be represented by the equation: $h = 16 - x^2$ factor the right hand side of this equation.

1. Factor: $13a^5 + 26ab^2 + 39b$ 1._____

2. Factor: $2x^2 - 4x - 8xy$ 2._____

3. Factor: $3ax + 3bx - 2a - 2b$ 3._____

4. Factor: $x^2y + x^2 + xy + x$ 4._____

5. Factor: $x^2 + 7x - 8$ 5._____

6. Factor: $k^2 - 2k - 10$ 6._____

7. Factor: $4a^2 - 28a + 24$ 7._____

8. Factor: $6z^2 + 5z + 1$ 8._____

9. Factor: $5k^2 + 7k + 2$ 9._____

10. Factor: $9b^3 + 30b^2 + 25b$ 10._____

11. Factor: $3m^2 - 12n^2$ 11._____

12. Factor: $m^5 - 25m$ 12._____

13. Factor: $d^3 - 64$ 13._____

14. Factor: $3x^4 + 24x$ 14._____

15. The height of a box with surface area of 108 square inches can be represented by the equation: $h = 25 - x^2$ factor the right hand side of this equation.

1. Reduce: $\dfrac{12ab^3c}{8a^2b}$

1._____

2. Reduce: $\dfrac{x+3}{-4(x+3)}$

2._____

3. Reduce: $\dfrac{3h+15}{h^2-25}$

3._____

4. Multiply: $\dfrac{9x^2y}{xy^3} \cdot \dfrac{x^2}{6y}$

4._____

5. Multiply: $\dfrac{(y+3)(y+2)}{y} \cdot \dfrac{3y^2}{y^2-y-12}$

5._____

6. Divide: $\dfrac{4x^2}{3y} \div \dfrac{2x}{9y^2}$

6._____

7. Divide: $\dfrac{c^2-9}{5c+15} \div \dfrac{c-3}{c+3}$

7._____

8.   Find the LCD of: $\dfrac{3}{k^2-4}$, and $\dfrac{2k}{k+2}$

8._____

9. Add: $\dfrac{2x+1}{x+1}+\dfrac{x+3}{x}$

9._____

10. Subtract: $\dfrac{3x}{x-5}-\dfrac{2x^2-8x}{x^2-9x+20}$

10._____

11. Solve the equation: $\dfrac{6}{a+4}-\dfrac{1}{2}=\dfrac{3}{a+4}$

11._____

12. Solve the equation: $\dfrac{3}{x}=\dfrac{2}{x+2}$

12._____

13. One inlet pipe can fill a chemical storage tank in 30 hours. Another inlet pipe can fill the same tank in 80 hours. How long will it take to fill the storage tank if the two pipes work together?

13._____

CHAPTER 9 FORM B   TECHNICAL MATH

NAME:_____   SECTION:_____

1. Reduce: $\dfrac{9x^2yz}{3x^2z}$ 1._____

2. Reduce: $\dfrac{a-4}{-4(a-4)}$ 2._____

3. Reduce: $\dfrac{2m+10}{m^2-25}$ 3._____

4. Multiply: $\dfrac{8a^2b}{ab^3}\cdot\dfrac{a^2}{6a}$ 4._____

5. Multiply: $\dfrac{(y+4)(y+2)}{y}\cdot\dfrac{3y^2}{y^2-4y-12}$ 5._____

6. Divide: $\dfrac{10m^2}{3k}\div\dfrac{5m}{12k^2}$ 6._____

7. Divide: $\dfrac{b^2-16}{5b+15}\div\dfrac{b-3}{b+4}$ 7._____

8.   Find the LCD of: $\dfrac{3}{x^2-25}$, and $\dfrac{2x}{x+5}$ 8._____

9. Add: $\dfrac{2y+1}{y+2}+\dfrac{y+3}{y}$ 9._____

10. Subtract: $\dfrac{3a}{a-3}-\dfrac{2a^2-8a}{a^2+2a-15}$ 10._____

11. Solve the equation: $\dfrac{1}{2y}-\dfrac{1}{y+1}=\dfrac{5}{2y^2+2y}$ 12._____

12. Solve the equation: $\dfrac{5}{k-1}=\dfrac{11}{k-2}$ 12._____

13. One inlet pipe can fill a chemical storage tank in 40 hours. Another inlet pipe can fill the same tank in 70 hours. How long will it take to fill the storage tank if the two pipes work together?

13._____

CHAPTER 10 FORM A TECHNICAL MATH

NAME:_____ SECTION:_____

1. Rewrite $4^{\frac{2}{3}}$ using radicals. 1._____

2. Rewrite $\sqrt{2x^5}$ using rational exponents 2._____

3. Simplify $\sqrt[3]{-216x^3}$ 3._____

4. Simplify $\sqrt[4]{32a^5b^{11}c^4}$ 4._____

5. Simplify $-\sqrt[3]{-64x^4y^3}$ 5._____

6. Simplify $\sqrt{-20}$ 6._____

7. Simplify $y^{\frac{1}{3}}y^{\frac{5}{6}}$ 7._____

8. Simplify $6\sqrt{5}-2\sqrt{20}+11\sqrt{5}$ 8._____

9. Simplify $\left(\sqrt{a}+3\sqrt{b}\right)^2$ 9._____

10. Rationalize $\sqrt{\dfrac{1}{2}}$ 10._____

11. Rationalize $\dfrac{5+\sqrt{2y}}{\sqrt{2y}}$ 11._____

12. Rationalize $\dfrac{4}{\sqrt{x+y}}$ 12._____

13. Solve the equation $\sqrt{x+4} = \sqrt{2x}$ 13._____

14. Solve the equation $\sqrt{x^2 + 5x} = x+5$ 14._____

15. The quadratic equation is given by the formula $x = \dfrac{-b \pm \sqrt{b^2 - 4ac}}{2a}$ evaluate this formula when a=1, b = 7, and c =10

1. Rewrite $7^{\frac{3}{2}}$ using radicals.   1._____

2. Rewrite $\sqrt{3x^3}$ using rational exponents   2._____

3. Simplify $\sqrt[3]{-64x^6}$ 3._____

4. Simplify $\sqrt[4]{48a^6b^5c^2}$ 4._____

5. Simplify $-\sqrt[3]{-27x^3y^4}$ 5._____

6. Simplify $\sqrt{-12}$ 6._____

7. Simplify $y^{\frac{1}{2}}y^{\frac{3}{4}}$ 7._____

8. Simplify $5\sqrt{18}-2\sqrt{12}+11\sqrt{3}$ 8._____

9. Simplify $\left(2\sqrt{a}+\sqrt{b}\right)^2$ 9._____

10. Rationalize $\sqrt{\dfrac{1}{3}}$

10._____

11. Rationalize $\dfrac{4+\sqrt{3x}}{\sqrt{3x}}$

11._____

12. Rationalize $\dfrac{5}{\sqrt{x}-y}$

12._____

13. Solve the equation $\sqrt{2x+5}=\sqrt{3x}$

13._____

14. Solve the equation $\sqrt{x^2+9x}=x+3$

14._____

15.   The quadratic equation is given by the formula $x=\dfrac{-b\pm\sqrt{b^2-4ac}}{2a}$ evaluate this formula when a=1, b = 5, and c =6

CHAPTER 11 FORM A	TECHNICAL MATH
NAME:_____	SECTION:_____

In questions 1-6 find the solution(s) to the quadratic equation, if they exist.

1. $x^2 + 7x + 10 = 0$ 1._____

2. $(R+3)^2 = 64$ 2._____

3. $k^2 + 2k = 5$ 3._____

4. $2x^2 + 4x + 3 = 0$ 4._____

5. $16x^2 = 25$ 5._____

6. What number must be added to the binomial $y^2 + 10y$
  in order to make it a perfect square trinomial?

                                                                     6._____

7. Find the vertex of: $y = -4x^2 + 8x - 3$ 7._____

8. Find the x-intercepts of: $y = -4x^2 + 8x - 3$ 8._____

9. Find the y-intercept of: $y = -4x^2 + 8x - 3$ 9._____

10. Find the axis of symmetry of: $y = -4x^2 + 8x - 3$ 10._____

11. Graph the quadratic equation: $y = -4x^2 + 8x - 3$ 11._____

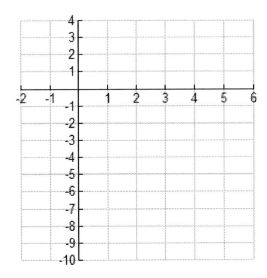

12. The length of a rectangle is 6 meters longer than the width. If the total area of the rectangle is 16m², find the dimensions of the rectangle.   12._____

13. An object is thrown from the top of a building. The function $s(t) = -16t^2 + 64$ models the height of the object at any time t. How long will it take for the object to reach the ground?

CHAPTER 11 FORM B   TECHNICAL MATH

NAME:_____   SECTION:_____

In questions 1-5 find the solution(s) to the quadratic equation, if they exist.

1. $x^2 - 5x + 6 = 0$ 1._____

2. $(R + 4)^2 = 36$ 2._____

3. $2k^2 + 4k = 10$ 3._____

4. $2x^2 + 4x + 7 = 0$ 4._____

5. $3x^2 - 150 = 0$ 5._____

6. What number should be added to the binomial $x^2 + 8x$
    in order to make it a perfect square trinomial?   6._____

7. Find the vertex of: $-4x^2 + 8x - 3$ 7._____

8. Find the x-intercepts of: $-4x^2 + 8x - 3$ 8._____

9. Find the y-intercept of: $-4x^2 + 8x - 3$ 9._____

10. Find the axis of symmetry of: $-4x^2+8x-3$ 10.

11. Graph the quadratic equation: $-4x^2+8x-3$ 11._____

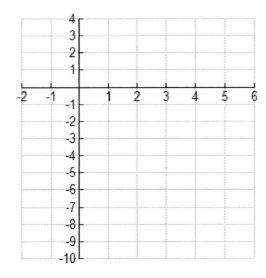

12. The length of a rectangle is 5 meters longer than the width. If the total area of the rectangle is 24m^2, find the dimensions of the rectangle.   12._____

13. An object is thrown from the top of a building. The function $s(t)=-16t^2+144$ models the height of the object at any time t. How long will it take for the object to reach the ground?

CHAPTER 12 FORM A	TECHNICAL MATH
NAME:_____	SECTION:_____

1. Identify the base of the exponential expression: $3(8)^x$ 1._____

2. Evaluate $y = 1.4(2.3)^x$ when $x = 1.75$ 2._____

3. Write the following equation in logarithmic form:
   $10^{2.67} = 467.74$ 3._____

4. Write in exponential form: $\log_4 64 = 3$ 4._____

5. Write as the sum, difference, or multiple of
   logarithms: $\log\left(\dfrac{4x}{5z^2}\right)$ 5._____

6. Express as a single logarithm: $\log \sqrt{a} + 3\log b$ 6._____

7. Solve the equation $2^{3x} = 7$ 7._____

8. Solve the equation $5^{4x+1} = 10$ 8._____

9. Solve the equation $\ln x - \ln\dfrac{1}{2} = 3$ 9._____

10. The formula $A = P\left(1 + \dfrac{r}{n}\right)^{nt}$ gives the amount of money A of an investment P after t years at an annual percentage rate r compounded n times per year. How long will it take $200 to grow into $1,000 at an annual percentage rate of 12% compounded twelve times a year?

10._____

11. In chemistry the formula of pH is: $pH = -\log\left[H^+\right]$ where H^+ is the concentration of the hydrogen ions. A mixture of acetic acid has a pH of 2.9. Find the concentration of hydrogen ions in the mixture.

11._____

CHAPTER 12 FORM B	TECHNICAL MATH
NAME:_____	SECTION:_____

1. Identify the base of the exponential expression: $2(5)^x$ 1._____

2. Evaluate $y = 1.7(3.1)^x$ when $x = 2.14$ 2._____

3. Write the following equation in logarithmic form:
   $$10^{1.54} = 34.67$$ 3._____

4. Write in exponential form: $\log_5 125 = 3$ 4._____

5. Write as the sum, difference, or multiple of

   logarithms: $\log\left(\dfrac{3a^2}{4c}\right)$ 5._____

6. Express as a single logarithm: $\log \sqrt[3]{a} + \log b$ 6._____

7. Solve the equation $2^{3x} = 7$ 7._____

8. Solve the equation $7^{2x+2} = 10$ 8._____

9. Solve the equation $\ln x - \ln \dfrac{1}{3} = 1$

9._____

10. The formula $A = P\left(1 + \dfrac{r}{n}\right)^{nt}$ gives the amount of money A of an investment P after t years at an annual percentage rate r compounded n times per year. How long will it take $300 to grow into $1200 at an annual percentage rate of 12% compounded twelve times a year?

10._____

11. In chemistry the formula of pH is: $pH = -\log\left[H^+\right]$ where H^+ is the concentration of the hydrogen ions. A mixture of acetic acid has a pH of 3.4. Find the concentration of hydrogen ions in the mixture.

11._____

CHAPTER 13 FORM A   TECHNICAL MATH

NAME:_____   SECTION:_____

1. Find the supplement of 127.3°   1._____

2. Use the figure below to find the measure of angle 3.

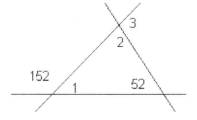

                                        2._____

3. Find the hypotenuse of a right triangle with legs of
   a = 5 and b =12.

                                        3._____

4. If a = 2.5 is a leg of a right triangle and c = 7.42 is the
   hypotenuse of a right triangle find the length of the missing
   leg to the nearest tenth.

                                        4._____

5. Find the $\sin 46.5°$ 5._____

6. If a=7.8, b= 3.2 are two legs of a right triangle find $\cos A$.   6._____

7. Find the csc A if $\tan A = \dfrac{5}{12}$ 7._____

8. Find the sec A if sin A = 0.8570   8._____

9.   Solve the right triangle if $\angle A = 47°$, $\angle C = 90°$ and b = 41.9.

                                                                     9._____

10. A ladder 25 feet long forms an angle 65 degrees with the ground.
     How far up the building does the ladder touch?

                                                                     10._____

11. The angle of elevation of the sun is 44.6 degrees. How long is
     the shadow of a building 111 feet tall?

                                                                     11._____

CHAPTER 13 FORM B	TECHNICAL MATH
NAME:_____	SECTION:_____

1. Find the supplement of $114.7°$

1._____

2. Use the figure below to find the measure of angle 3.

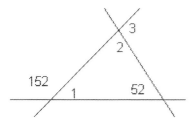

2._____

3. Find the hypotenuse of a right triangle with legs of
    a = 8 and b = 15

3._____

4. If a = 3.5 is a leg of a right triangle and c =8.42 is the
    hypotenuse of a right triangle find the length of the missing
    leg to the nearest tenth.

4._____

5. Find the cos 43.5^0

5._____

6. If a=7.8, b= 3.2 are two legs of a right triangle find cos B.

6._____

7. Find the csc A if tan A = $\dfrac{8}{15}$

7._____

8. Find the csc A if cos A = 0.8570   8._____

9.   Solve the right triangle if $\angle A = 47^{o}$, $\angle C = 90^{o}$ and b = 41.9.

                                                                        9._____

10. A ladder 15 feet long forms an angle 65 degrees with the ground.
    How far up the building does the ladder touch?

                                                                        10._____

11. The angle of elevation of the sun is 44.6 degrees. How long is
    the shadow of a building 134 feet tall?

                                                                        11._____

CHAPTER 14 FORM A   TECHNICAL MATH

NAME:_____   SECTION:_____

1. If the terminal side of an angle, θ, passes through
   the point $(-8,15)$ find $\sec \theta$.   1._____

2. If $\tan \theta > 0$ and $\sin \theta < 0$, in what quadrant does
   θ lie?   2._____

3. Find the reference angle for 213.4^o 3._____

4. Find θ to the nearest tenth of a degree if $\cos \theta = -0.5616$
   and $\sin \theta < 0$.   4._____

5. Given the following properties of a triangle find Angle B.
   $a = 47.1$ $b = 34.0$ $A = 69.1^o$ 5._____

6. Given the following properties of a triangle find Angle C.
   $a = 47.1$ $b = 34.0$ $A = 69.1^o$ 6._____

7. Given the following properties of a triangle find side c..
   $a = 47.1$ $b = 34.0$ $A = 69.1^o$ 7._____

8. Given the following properties of a triangle find angle A
   $a = 119$ $b = 156$ $c = 205$
                                                              8._____

9. Given the following properties of a triangle find angle C
   $a = 119$ $b = 156$ $c = 205$ 9._____

10.   A vector has a magnitude of 27.6 and an angle of 320.5^o.
    Resolve the vector into its x component and y component.
                                                              10._____

11. An engineer believes a cell phone tower is not exactly perpendicular to the ground. He drops a line from the top of the 70 ft tower and finds the line hits the ground 3.66 feet from the base of the cell phone tower. How many degrees is the angle formed by the tower and the ground?

11._____

CHAPTER 14 FORM B   TECHNICAL MATH

NAME:_____   SECTION:_____

1. If the terminal side of an angle, θ, passes through
   the point $(-5,12)$ find $\sec \theta$.   1._____

2. If $\tan \theta < 0$ and $\sin \theta < 0$, in what quadrant does
   θ lie?   2._____

3. Find the reference angle for 347.5° 3._____

4. Find θ to the nearest tenth of a degree if $\cos \theta = -0.5293$
   and $\sin \theta < 0$.   4._____

5. Given the following properties of a triangle find Angle C.
   $A = 68.41^{\circ}$ $B = 54.23^{\circ}$ $a = 12.75$ 5._____

6. Given the following properties of a triangle find side b.
   $A = 68.41^{\circ}$ $B = 54.23^{\circ}$ $a = 12.75$ 6._____

7. Given the following properties of a triangle find side c.
   $A = 68.41^{\circ}$ $B = 54.23^{\circ}$ $a = 12.75$ 7._____

8. Given the following properties of a triangle find angle A.
   $a = 119$ $b = 156$ $c = 123$
                                                              8._____

9. Given the following properties of a triangle find angle B.
   $a = 119$ $b = 156$ $c = 123$ 9._____

10.   A vector has a magnitude of 12.5 and an angle of -44.5^o.
        Resolve the vector into its x component and y component.

                                             10._____

11. An engineer believes a cell phone tower is not exactly perpendicular to the ground. He drops a line from the top of the 70 ft tower and finds the line hits the ground 3.66 feet from the base of the cell phone tower. How many degrees is the angle formed by the tower and the ground?

                                             11._____

CHAPTER 15 FORM A	TECHNICAL MATH
NAME:_____	SECTION:_____

1. Convert 75° to radians. Leave your answer in
   terms of π.   1._____

2. Convert 2.5 radians to degrees   2._____

3. Evaluate $\cos\dfrac{\pi}{4}$.   3._____

4. Find the length of an arc with a radius of 13.2 in and a
   central angle of $\dfrac{\pi}{4}$.   4._____

5. Find the area of a sector with central angle $\dfrac{5\pi}{4}$ and a radius
   of 4.78m.   5._____

6. A blenders blade is 2.5 inches long and rotates at 5000
   revolutions per minute. What is the linear velocity of a
   a point on the end of the blade?   6._____

7. What is the amplitude of the graph of $y = -3\sin \pi x$?   7._____

8. Graph $y = -4\sin x$

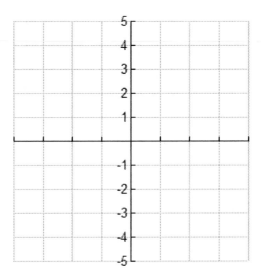

9. What is the period of the graph of $y = 3\sin \pi x$?   9._____

10. Find a possible equation of the graph. Each has mark on the x-axis represents $\dfrac{\pi}{2}$ below:

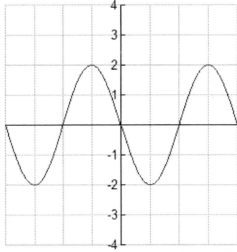

11. Find the displacement of $y = -3\cos\left(4\pi - \dfrac{1}{4}\right)$ 11._____

1. Convert 65° to radians. Leave your answer in
    terms of π.   1._____

2. Convert 1.75 radians to degrees   2._____

3. Evaluate $\sin\dfrac{\pi}{4}$.   3._____

4. Find the length of an arc with a radius of 14.6in. and a
    central angle of $\dfrac{\pi}{6}$.   4._____

5. Find the area of a sector with central angle $\dfrac{5\pi}{4}$ and a radius
    of 8.21m.   5._____

6. A blenders blade is 1.5 inches long and rotates at 4500
    revolutions per minute. What is the linear velocity of a
    a point on the end of the blade?   6._____

7. What is the amplitude of the graph of $y = -2\sin\pi x$?   7._____

8. Graph $y = -3\sin x$

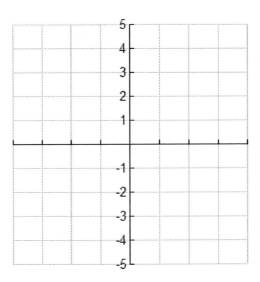

9. What is the period of the graph of $y = 3\cos \pi x$?   9._____

10. Find a possible equation of the graph below. Each hash mark represents $\dfrac{\pi}{2}$.:

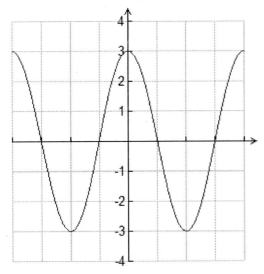

11. Find the displacement of $y = -0.5\cos\left(7\pi - \dfrac{1}{7}\right)$ 11._____

CHAPTER 16 FORM A   TECHNICAL MATH

NAME:_____   SECTION:_____

1. Simplify j^{34} 1._____

2. Simplify $\sqrt{-12}$ 2._____

3. What is the conjugate of $-1+j$?   3._____

4. Add: $(3+5j)+(-2+6j)$ 4._____

5. Multiply: $(1+j)(3-4j)$ 5._____

6. Multiply: $4j(5-2j)$ 6._____

7. Divide: $\dfrac{(3+8j)}{(2-2j)}$ 7._____

8. Simplify: $(-3-j)^2$ 8._____

9. Use the graph to add $(5-4j)+(-3-6j)$

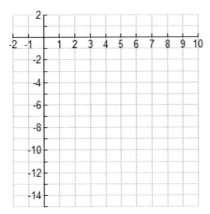

10. Convert the complex number $(2+3j)$ to polar form.   10._____

11. Express the abbreviation $12.2 \operatorname{cis} 174.3^{o}$ as a polar number.

11._____

12. Convert the polar number $1.35\left(\cos 235^{o}+i\sin 235^{o}\right)$ to rectangular form.

12._____

13. An alternating current has an impedance of $11+11j$ amperes and a current of $-4+7j$ ohms. If the voltage is the product of impedance and current find the voltage of this alternating circuit.

13_____

1. Simplify j^{30}

1._____

2. Simplify $\sqrt{-18}$

2._____

3. What is the conjugate of $-2+j$?

3._____

4. Add: $(2+7j)+(-3+4j)$

4._____

5. Multiply: $(1+j)(3+6j)$

5._____

6. Multiply: $3j(4-3j)$

6._____

7. Divide: $\dfrac{(5+4j)}{(3-3j)}$

7._____

8. Simplify: $(-2-j)^2$

8._____

9. Use the graph to add $(5-4j)+(-3-6j)$

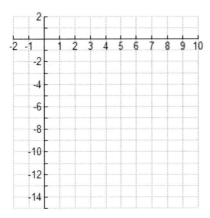

10. Convert the complex number $(3+2j)$ to polar form.   10._____

11. Express the abbreviation $11.7 \operatorname{cis} 164.5^{\circ}$ as a polar number.

11._____

12. Convert the polar number $2.75\left(\cos 315^{\circ}+i\sin 315^{\circ}\right)$ to rectangular form.

12._____

13. An alternating current has an impedance of $10+10j$ amperes and a current of $-5+9j$ ohms. If the voltage is the product of impedance and current find the voltage of this alternating circuit.

13_____

CHAPTER 17 FORM A	TECHNICAL MATH
NAME:_____	SECTION:_____

1. The following lists the number of organ transplants given in 2006. Use this data to construct a pie chart.

Type	Number
Kidney	14,376
Liver	5614
Heart	1852
Lung	1220
Total	23,062

Use the following information to answer questions 2-10. 24 students in an engineering class were asked to record the number of hours spent in a lab during a week. The results are listed below.

3, 10, 21, 14, 8, 5, 1, 4, 13, 7, 9, 6, 11, 10, 6, 7, 12, 16, 1 , 7, 14, 1, 11, 8

2. . Construct a frequency distribution for the data using 5 classes.

3. Find the mean of the data set.   3._____

4. Find the median of the data set.   4._____

5. Find the mode of the data set.   5._____

6. Find the range of the data set.   6._____

7. Find the sample standard deviation of the data set.   7._____

8. If one of the students is selected at random what is
    the probability he or she spent exactly 3 hours in the lab?   8._____

9. If one student is selected at random what is the probability
    that he or she spent at least 10 hours in the lab?   9._____

10. If one of student is selected at random what is the probability
    that he or she spent between 10 and 20 hours in the lab?   10._____

1. The following lists the number of organ transplants given in 2006. Use this data to construct a pie chart.

Type	Number
Kidney	14,376
Liver	5614
Heart	1852
Lung	1220
Total	23,062

Use the following information to answer questions 2-10.   24 students in an engineering class were asked to record the number of hours spent in a lab during a week. The results are listed below.

3, 10, 21, 14, 8, 5, 1, 4, 13, 7, 9, 6, 11, 10, 6, 7, 12, 16, 1 , 7, 14, 1, 11, 8

2. . Construct a frequency distribution for the data using 5 classes.

3. Find the mean of the data set.   3._____

4. Find the median of the data set.   4._____

5. Find the mode of the data set.   5._____

6. Find the range of the data set.   6._____

7. Find the sample standard deviation of the data set.   7._____

8. If one of the students is selected at random what is
    the probability he or she spent exactly 11 hours in the lab?   8._____

9. If one student is selected at random what is the probability
    that he or she spent at least 5 hours in the lab?   9._____

10. If one of student is selected at random what is the probability
     that he or she spent between 0 and 10 hours in the lab?   10._____

Chapter 1 Signed Numbers
Answer Key: **Form A**

Answer Key: **Form B**

Form A	Form B
1. 8	1. 6
2. 1	2. 1
3. 7	3. 7
4. -4	4. 1
5. 12	5. 10
6. 0	6. 0
7. $\dfrac{9}{16}$	7. $\dfrac{4}{25}$
8. $-\dfrac{4}{25}$	8. $-\dfrac{9}{16}$
9. 2	9. 2
10. 0.730	10. 0.910
11. 4.37	11. 4.70 *? 4.69*
12. 1.74×10^{10}	12. 1.47×10^{10}
13. 4.3×10^{7}	13. 3.4×10^{7} *3.4×10^{-6}*
14. 21,700,000	14. 712,000
15. 7.56×10^{5}	15. 3.77×10^{5}
16. 9.33×10^{-3}	16. 9.243×10^{-3}
17. 8.64×10^{8}	17. 2.236×10^{9}
18. 2.4×10^{-7} *? 2.5×10^{-7}*	18. 2.5×10^{-4}
19. 84.5	19. 78
20. 1.3×10^{-3} seconds.	20. 2.205×10^{-3} seconds *?*

Chapter 2 Approximate Numbers

Answer Key: **Form A**	Answer Key: **Form B**
1. 4	1. 5
2. 2	2. 2
3. 76	3. 1.5
4. 0.240	4. 10.9
5. micro Liters	5. mega ohms
6. millivolts	6. mV
7. 15.24 cm	7. 31.3 cm
8. 0.25 square feet	8. 0.5 square feet
9. 20.51 mph	9. 20.5 mph
10. 8.2 mph	10. 12.3 mph
11. 2.46	11. 6.42
12. 2007	12. 2115
13. 1000 grams	13. $\dfrac{1}{1000}$ L
14. 1473 feet	14. 1670 feet
15. 0.00180 watts	15. 0.00360 Volts

Chapter 3: Intro. to Algebra
Answer Key: **Form A**

1. -7

2. $16t^2u, 3t^2u$

3. $19x^2$

4. $-3xyz$

5. $7a^4b^4$

6. $t^3 + 2t^2 + 6t$

7. $-6x^2y^3$

8. $2y^2 + 3y - 9$

9. $2x^3 + 2x^2 - 24x$

10. $r^2 - 25$

11. $\dfrac{-4a^2}{b}$

12. $\dfrac{a}{3b} - \dfrac{1}{2} - \dfrac{3b}{4a}$

13. $y - 7$

14. $5r^2 - 7r - 9$

15. $8x + 16$

Answer Key: **Form B**

1. -10

2. $14w^2v, 5w^2v$

3. $18y^2$

4. $-4abc$

5. $5x^4y^4$

6. $8k^3 - 15k^4 + 6k$

7. $-35x^2y^3$

8. $3x^2 + 7x - 20$

9. $a^2 + 2a - 8$

10. $h^2 - 16$

11. $\dfrac{-6x^2}{y^2}$

12. $-2a^2 - 3ab + 5b^3$

13. $a - 3$

14. $13r^2 - 30r - 11$

15. $10y + 25$

Chapter 4 Equations and Inequalities

Answer Key: **Form A**	Answer Key: **Form B**
1. $t = 3$	1. $t = -2$
2. $w = -8$	2. $w = 32$
3. $x = 9$	3. $x = 2$
4. $x = 5$	4. $x = 5$
5. $t = \dfrac{I}{\mathrm{Pr}}$	5. $r = \dfrac{I}{Pt}$
6. $r = \dfrac{A - P}{P}$	6. $A = \dfrac{J + 3}{C}$
7. $h = \dfrac{2k}{(a + b)}$	7. $k = \dfrac{5K}{(x + y)}$
8. $M = \dfrac{F}{f} - 1$	8. $L = \dfrac{S}{n} - 2$
9. $k \le 4$	9. $k \le 5$
10. $y < 15$	10. $y < -17$
11. $m \ge 20$	11. $n \ge 20$
12. $17 : 2$	12. $15 : 4$
13. $4 : 1$	13. $3 : 2$
14. $x = 120$	14. $x = 84$
15. $y = 11$	15. $y = 11$
16. $k = -5.6$	16. $k = -5.6$
17. $172.25	17. $176.25
18. 500 gigabytes	18. 600 gigabytes
19. 1 hour	20. 2 hours
20. $24,000	20. $11,0000

Chapter 5 Graphs
Answer Key: **Form A**   Answer Key: **Form B**

1. -18   1. -32

2. 12   2. 11

3. $[4,\infty)$ 3. $[-3,\infty)$

4. $t \neq 0$ 4. $t \neq 0$

5. Quadrant II   5. Quadrant I

6. (-1, 0)   6. (5,0)

7. E   7. E

8. (7, - 8)   8. (7, -8)

9.
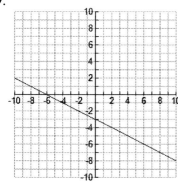

9.
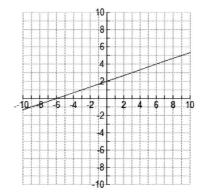

10.
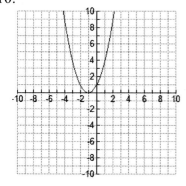

10.
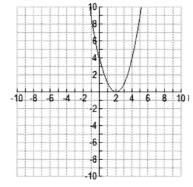

11. $\dfrac{4}{5}$ 11. $\dfrac{4}{5}$

12. $\left(\dfrac{-10}{3}, 0\right)$

12. $(2, 0)$

13. $(0, 5)$

13. $\left(0, \dfrac{8}{3}\right)$

14. 3 Seconds

14. 2 Seconds

15. $6000

15. $6000

Chapter 6 Introduction to Geometry.

Answer Key: **Form A**

1. 47.8°

2. 137°26'

3. 17.5 cm

4. 23 ft

5. 28.89 m

6. 52.46yd^2

7. 1.7m^2

8. 3698 mm^2

9. 7790.8 in^3

10. 351.69cm^3

11. 1920.5yd^3

12. $465.00

Answer Key: **Form B**

1. 36.1°

2. 41°21'

3. 28cm

4. 23 ft

5. 42.7cm

6. 44.94yd^2

7. 3.77m^2

8. 3698 mm^2

9. 1108.72in^3

10. 482.28 cm^3

11. 876.5m^3

12. $980.00

Chapter 7 Simultaneous Equations
Answer Key: **Form A**   Answer Key: **Form B**

1.

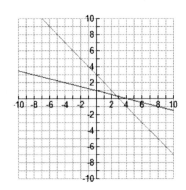

1.

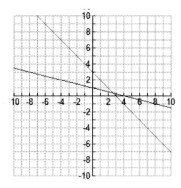

2. $k = -1, j = 4$

3. $w = 2, v = 5$

4. inconsistent

5. $x = 3.6, y = -0.2$

6. $x = 3, y = 1$

7. inconsistent

8. 4

9. 8

10. $a = 1, b = 2$

11. 700

12. $14,000

2. $x = -1, y = 4$

3. $x = 2, y = 5$

4. inconsistent

5. $x = 3.6, y = -0.2$

6. $x = -7, y = -11$

7. inconsistent

8. 6

9. 2

10. $a = -1, b = -2$

11. 1500

12. $10,000

Chapter 8 Factoring
Answer Key: **Form A**

Answer Key: **Form B**

1. $17\left(x^5 + 2xy^2 + 3y\right)$

1. $13\left(a^5 + 2ab^2 + 3b\right)$

2. $2y\left(2y - 4 - x\right)$

2. $2x(x - 2 - 4y)$

3. $\left(a + b\right)\left(2x - 3\right)$

3. $\left(a + b\right)\left(3x - 2\right)$

4. $a\left(a - 1\right)\left(b + 1\right)$

4. $x\left(x + 1\right)\left(y + 1\right)$

5. $\left(b + 7\right)\left(b - 1\right)$

5. $\left(x - 8\right)\left(x + 1\right)$

6. $(x - 4)(x + 3)$

6. $\left(k - 5\right)\left(k + 2\right)$

7. $3\left(y - 6\right)\left(y - 1\right)$

7. $4(a - 2)(a - 3)$

8. $\left(4z + 1\right)\left(z + 3\right)$

8. $\left(2a + 1\right)\left(3a + 1\right)$

9. $\left(2k + 1\right)\left(3k + 2\right)$

9. $\left(5k + 2\right)\left(k + 1\right)$

10. $a\left(4a + 5\right)^2$

10. $b\left(3b + 5\right)^2$

11. $2\left(a + 2b\right)\left(a - 2b\right)$

11. $3\left(m + 2n\right)\left(m - 2n\right)$

12. $m\left(m^2 + 3\right)\left(m^2 - 3\right)$

12. $m\left(m^2 + 5\right)\left(m^2 - 5\right)$

13. $\left(c - 3\right)\left(c^2 + 3c + 9\right)$

13. $(d - 3)(d^2 + 3d + 9)$

14. $2y\left(y + 4\right)\left(y^2 - 4y + 16\right)$

14. $3x\left(x + 2\right)\left(x^2 - 2x + 4\right)$

15. $\left(4 + x\right)\left(4 - x\right)$

15. $\left(5 - x\right)\left(5 + x\right)$

Chapter 9 Rational Expressions and Equations
Answer Key: **Form A**   Answer Key: **Form B**

1. $\dfrac{3b^2c}{2a}$ 1. $3y$

2. $-\dfrac{1}{4}$ 2. $-\dfrac{1}{4}$

3. $\dfrac{3}{h-5}$ 3. $\dfrac{2}{m-5}$

4. $\dfrac{3x^3}{2y^3}$ 4. $\dfrac{4a^2}{3b^2}$

5. $\dfrac{3(y+2)}{(y-4)}$ 5. $\dfrac{3(y+4)}{(y-6)}$

6. $6xy$ 6. $8mk$

7. $\dfrac{c+3}{5}$ 7. $\dfrac{b-4}{5}$

8. $-\dfrac{4}{25}$ 8. $-\dfrac{9}{16}$

9. $\dfrac{3x^2+5x+3}{x(x+1)}$ 9. $\dfrac{3y^2+6y+6}{y(y+2)}$

10. $\dfrac{x^2-20x}{(x-5)(x-4)}$ 10. $\dfrac{a+27}{(a+5)(a-3)}$

11. $a = 2$ 11. $y = 4$

12. $x = -6$ 12. $k = \dfrac{1}{6}$

13. 21.8 hours   13. 25.5 hours

Chapter 10 Radicals
Answer Key: **Form A**   Answer Key: **Form B**

1. $\left(\sqrt[3]{4}\right)^{2}$ or $\sqrt[3]{16}$

2. $2^{\frac{1}{2}}x^{\frac{5}{2}}$

3. $-6x$

4. $2abc\sqrt[4]{2ab^{3}c}$

5. $4xy\sqrt[3]{x}$

6. $2i\sqrt{5}$

7. $y^{\frac{4}{3}}$

8. $13\sqrt{5}$

9. $a+6\sqrt{ab}+9b$

10. $\dfrac{\sqrt{2}}{2}$

11. $\dfrac{5\sqrt{2y}+2y}{2y}$

12. $\dfrac{4(\sqrt{x}-y)}{x-y^{2}}$

13. $x=4$

14. $x=-5$

15. $x=-2,\ \ x=-5$

1. $\left(\sqrt{7}\right)^{3}$ or $\sqrt{343}$

2. $3^{\frac{1}{2}}x^{\frac{3}{2}}$

3. $-4x^{2}$

4. $2ab\sqrt[4]{3a^{2}bc^{2}}$

5. $3xy\sqrt[3]{y}$

6. $2i\sqrt{3}$

7. $y^{\frac{5}{4}}$

8. $17\sqrt{3}$

9. $4a+4\sqrt{ab}+b$

10. $\dfrac{\sqrt{3}}{3}$

11. $\dfrac{4\sqrt{3x}+3x}{3x}$

12. $\dfrac{5(\sqrt{x}-y)}{x-y^{2}}$

13. $x=5$

14. $x=3$

15. $x=-2,\ \ x=-3$

Chapter 11 Quadratic Equations

Answer Key: **Form A**   Answer Key: **Form B**

1. $x = -2, x = -5$ 1. $x = 2, x = 3$

2. $R = 5, R = -11$ 2. $R = 2, R = -10$

3. $k = -1 \pm \sqrt{6}$ 3. $k = -1 \pm \sqrt{6}$

4. $x = \dfrac{-2 \pm i\sqrt{2}}{2}$ 4. $x = \dfrac{-2 \pm i\sqrt{10}}{2}$

5. $x = \pm \dfrac{5}{4}$ 5. $x = \pm 5\sqrt{2}$

6. 25   6. 16

7. (1,1)   7. (1,1)

8. $\left(\dfrac{1}{2}, 0\right)$, $\left(\dfrac{3}{2}, 0\right)$ 8. $\left(\dfrac{1}{2}, 0\right)$, $\left(\dfrac{3}{2}, 0\right)$

9. (0, -3)   9. (0, -3)

10. x = 1   10. x = 1

11.   11.

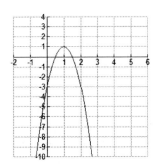   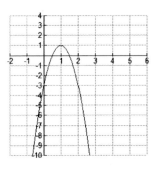

Chapter 12 Radicals
Answer Key: **Form A**

Answer Key: **Form B**

1. 8

2. 5

2. 6.01

2. 19.14

3. $\log_{10} 467.74 = 2.67$

3. $\log_{10} 34.67 = 1.54$

4. $4^3 = 64$

4. $5^3 = 125$

5. $\log 4 + \log x - \log 5 - 2\log z$

5. $\log 3 + 2\log a - \log 4 - \log c$

6. $\log \sqrt{ab^3}$

6. $\log a^{\frac{1}{3}}b$

7. 0.9358

7. 0.936

8. 0.1077

8. -0.408

9. $x = 10.04$

9. $x = 0.906$

10. 13.5 years

10. 11.6 years

11. 0.00125

11. 0.0004

Chapter 13 Right Angle Trigonometry
Answer Key: **Form A**   Answer Key: **Form B**

1. $52.7°$ 1. $65.3°$

2. $100°$ 2. $100°$

3. c = 13   3. 17

4. 7.0   4. 7.66

5. 0.7254   5. 0.7254

6. 0.2619   6. 0.9286

7. $\dfrac{13}{5}$ 7. $\dfrac{17}{8}$

8. 1.9406   8. 2.0657

9. B = 53, a = 44.49, C = 60.84   9. B = 53, a = 44.9, c = 61.4

10. 22.66 ft.   10. 13.59 ft.

11. 109.46ft   11. 132.14 ft.

Chapter 14 Right Angle Trigonometry
Answer Key: **Form A**   Answer Key: **Form B**

1. $-\dfrac{17}{8}$ 1. $\dfrac{5}{13}$

2. Quadrant 3   2. Quadrant 4

3. 33.4   3. 12.5

4. 235.8   4. 121.96

5. 42.4   5. 57.36

6. 68.5   6. 11.13

7. 46.9   7. 11.55

8. 35.3   8. 48.7

9. 95.4   9. 80.3

10. x = 21.3   y = -17.6   10. x = 8.9   y = -8.8

11. 87   11. 87

Chapter 15 Trig Functions
Answer Key: **Form A**

Answer Key: **Form B**

1. $\dfrac{5\pi}{12}$

2. $\dfrac{13\pi}{36}$

2. 143.24

2. 100

3. $\dfrac{\sqrt{2}}{2}$

3. $\dfrac{\sqrt{2}}{2}$

4. 10.37

4. 7.64

5. 44.86 m^2

5. 132.3 m^2

6. 78,500 in/mi or about 74 mi/hr

6. 42,390 in/min or about 40 mi/hr

7. 3

7. 2

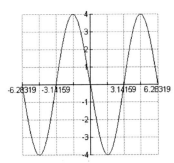

8.

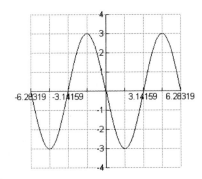

8.

9. 2

9. 2

10. y = -2sin x (answers can vary)

10. y = 3cos x (answers can vary)

11. $\dfrac{1}{16}$

11. $\dfrac{1}{49}$

Chapter 16 Complex Numbers
Answer Key: **Form A**   Answer Key: **Form B**

1. -1   2. -1

2. $2i\sqrt{3}$ 2. $3i\sqrt{2}$

3. -1-j   3. -2 –j

4. 1+11j   4. -1+11j

5. 7- j   5. -3 + 9j

6. 8 + 20j   6. 12j + 9

7. $\dfrac{11}{4}+\dfrac{11}{4}j$ 7. $\dfrac{1}{6}+\dfrac{3}{2}j$

8. 8 + 6j   8. 3 + 4j

9. graphs will vary   9. graphs will vary
    2 – 10j   2 – 10j

10. $\sqrt{13}$ cis 56.3   10. $\sqrt{13}$ cis 33.7

11. $12.2\left(\cos174.3^{o}+i\sin174.3^{o}\right)$ 11. $11.7\left(\cos164.5^{o}+i\sin164.5^{o}\right)$

12. -0.77 – 1.1j   12. 1.9 – 1.9j

13. 121 + 33j   13. -140 + 40j

Chapter 17 Data Analysis

Answer Key: **Form A**	Answer Key: **Form B**
1. Answers will vary	1. Answers will vary
2.	2.

Class	Frequency
1-5	6
6-10	10
11-15	6
16-20	1
21-25	1

Form A	Form B
3. 8.54	3. 8.54
4. 8	4. 8
5. 1	5. 1
6. 20	6. 20
7. 5	7. 5
8. 1/24	8. 1/12
9. 5/12	9. 19/24
10. 3/8	10. 2/3